Basic Electronics

Book 1 **Introducing Electronics**
Measuring Instruments

Basic Electronics is published in five parts:

Book 1 — sections A and B
Introducing Electronics. Measuring Instruments

Book 2 — sections C and D
Resistors in Circuits. Capacitors in Circuits

Book 3 — sections E and F
Inductors in Circuits. Diodes in Circuits

Book 4 — sections G and H
Meters. Voltage-dividers

Book 5 — sections I, J, and K
Transistors in Circuits. Transistors in Action. Post-transistor Projects

The course was prepared by Malcolm Plant, a member of the central team of Project Technology, and was based on earlier work on the teaching of electronics by Douglas Shorthouse.

Project
Technology

Basic Electronics
Book 1 **Introducing Electronics**
Measuring Instruments

The English Universities Press Ltd/
Schools Council

ISBN 0 340 18249 0

First printed 1975

The English Universities Press Ltd
St Paul's House, Warwick Lane, London EC4P 4AH

Set in IBM Press Roman by Tecprint Ltd, Loughborough
Printed and bound in Great Britain
by Clarke, Doble and Brendon Ltd, Plymouth

CONTENTS

Section B: Measuring instruments

Section A
Introducing Electronics

Quick route
If you want to follow a quicker route through Section A, you can omit the material between the symbols ▽ and △ in the left-hand margin (Section A7). Return to this material if you require more detailed information about electrons.

A1 WHY STUDY ELECTRONICS?

A1.1 The Electronic Age

While some of the world's people appear happy and contented without being more closely involved with electronics than seeing the occasional lightning flash, many of you reading this may well feel that electronic apparatus of one sort or another rules your lives. In fact, so powerful is the influence of electronics that the age in which we live is often called the *Electronic Age*; it is also called the *Space Age* and the *Atomic Age*, but neither description is as apt as the first, since both space travel and electrical energy from atomic power would be impossible to control without the services of electronics.

It will help you to understand how dependent modern society is on the services of electronics if we look at its contribution to five main areas of technology:

consumer electronics,
communications electronics,
computer electronics,
control electronics,
caring electronics.

A1.2 Consumer electronics

The majority of us personally recognise that rapid advances are being made in the field of electronics through the goods we buy; to the electronics industry this makes us the so-called 'consumers' of electronic equipment. The continual improvements we notice in the design and performance of cassette tape-recorders, record-players, and electronic wrist-watches, for example, illustrate how we, the consumers, benefit from the remarkable skills of the electronics engineer. Fig. A1.1 shows an electronic wrist-watch which has no moving parts; the time and date are displayed on what is known as a *liquid crystal*. A watch like this is able to operate for over a year on a small internal battery.

A1.3 Communications electronics

It is well worthwhile pausing from time to time to consider how amazing it is to be able to carry in the palm of the hand a device which will receive the voice and music of people thousands of kilometres away. But, more impressive than that, artificial satellites acting as relay-stations in orbit round the earth are beaming TV pictures from continent to continent; we cannot fail to be impressed with our ability to watch the fortunes of athletes competing in the Olympic Games on the other side of the world.

Fig. A1.1 The solid-state electronic watch, having no moving parts. It is guaranteed to have an accuracy of 1/10 second a day, and operates for a year from an internal battery. *(Courtesy Rastra Electronics Ltd)*

Space travel has broken all records for long-distance radio and TV communication. We have been treated to the driver's eye view of the lunar panorama as an astronaut steers his car round the craters on the Moon; Mariner 9 has sent back thousands of detailed pictures of the surface of Mars; and Pioneer 10 – an unmanned spacecraft sent to the planet Jupiter via Mars and the asteroid belt – during its fly-by of Jupiter in December 1973, sent back pictures of this planet, as well as making other measurements at over five times the distance of the Earth from the Sun. How did Pioneer 10 know when to start taking pictures? A signal was sent out from the Earth to switch on its camera. In fact, it is hoped that a two-way communication will be maintained with Pioneer 10 as it travels out to the fringes of the Solar System. Fig. A1.2 shows the type of large aerial which is required to pick up the weak signals from artificial satellites and space probes.

A1.4 Computer electronics

As our technological society becomes more complex, the information about it which has to be processed and stored multiplies. In fact, information storage and its retrieval is becoming a major problem to the scientist, the policeman, the librarian, and to other people who have to handle large amounts of information.

Fig. A1.2 Goonhilly Downs Radio Station, Cornwall. Satellite-signal receiving aerial no. 2.
(Courtesy Ministry of Posts and Telecommunications)

Computers have grown in number and memory capacity to meet this need. They
are now a necessity. They relieve the boredom of filing and retrieving information;
they save space by storing the information in digital form in an electronic
memory — magnetic and semiconductor memories are common; and they work
fast, times for access to the 'store' of the computer being as short as one millionth
of a second.

A digital computer stores information in 'bits' and operates on these bits. A
'bit' is a 'binary digit' and belongs to the 'binary code', based on the two digits
0 and 1. A mathematician wishing to use a computer to make rapid and repeated
calculations will use a *digital computer,* and so will the banker or the policeman

Fig. A1.3 Electronic calculator. *(Courtesy Hewlett-Packard Ltd)*

when storing coded information about money transactions or crime statistics, say. But an engineer may require to test the performance of a new bridge design by setting up a mathematical model. He will use an *analogue computer* which examines what happens when conditions to his model are continuously altered. In this way he can predict the behaviour of the real bridge under the combined effect of wind, traffic, and the other stresses it has to withstand. Fig. A1.3 shows one of the advantages of living in the Computer Age (yes, it has been called that too). It might seem that the slide-rule and the mathematical tables can be put away and you can forget your 'times' tables. Calculators like the one shown here appear to be able to do most of the calculations we shall ever want to do in everyday life.

A1.5 Control electronics

You will probably realise that it is not possible to separate this category from computer electronics or from communications electronics; in fact, the five 'electronic C's' we are considering are often seen to be working together. For instance, communication is essential for radio control; computers provide control signals; and an ordinary transistor radio incorporates automatic volume control.

Control is an absolutely essential part of the operation of any reliable man-made system. Electronic control mechanisms enable aircraft to land in poor visibility; processes in chemical factories depend on electronic control at various stages of the production of chemicals; and the safe and reliable operation of an atomic power station requires electronic control to monitor temperatures, pressures, etc. within its core, to guard against it 'running away' and perhaps exploding – see fig. A1.4.

There are many examples of electronic control in the home. Electrical power to lights, fires, drills, etc., can be controlled at the twist of a knob; temperature and humidity in the home or greenhouse may be automatically controlled by electronic circuits; and washing machines are electronically programmed to carry out a pre-arranged sequence of washing instructions.

Fig. A1.4 The control room of the Oldbury Nuclear Power Station situated on the River Severn in Gloucestershire. The station provides 600 MW (million watts) of electrical power. *(Courtesy Central Electricity Generating Board)*

A1.6 Caring electronics

It is important that electronics is made to work for relieving human suffering as well as for providing a better world in which to live. So 'caring' electronics means electronics designed to help the sick, although a more sophisticated description is 'medical electronics'.

Fig. A1.5 shows how miniaturisation in electronics has provided an aid for the blind person — his 'electronic eye'. Fig. A1.6 shows another device for keeping the heart of someone suffering from heart disease beating regularly.

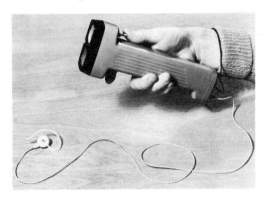

Fig. A1.5 Electronic 'stick' for a blind person. This 'torch' helps a blind person to move around by emitting ultra-sonic waves which are reflected by objects around him. He hears sounds of changing pitch which, with practice, tell him the distances and nature of these objects. *(Courtesy Dr J.D. Armstrong)*

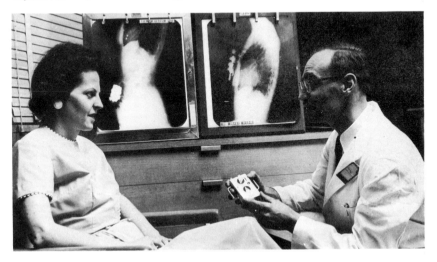

Fig. A1.6 The patient on the left has a heart pacemaker stitched inside the body, as shown by the left-hand X-ray photo. The physician is holding an external pacemaker, positioned as shown by the X-ray photo on the right. *(Courtesy USIS)*

7

A1.7 Questions for you to answer

1 Why is it wrong to call a transistor radio just a 'transistor'?

2 Why is there a lower limit to the size of a wrist-watch, a portable television, or an electronic pocket calculator. Do you think this limit has been reached?

3 In what ways does electronics help the doctor? What is a 'pacemaker' and an 'electrocardiograph'? How do they get their names?

4 What are 'bugging' devices? Why are people worried about their use?

5 How does electronics help to ease the problems of disabled people?

6 Why is it desirable to have cars under automatic control on motorways?

7 How does 'solid-state' electronics compare with 'vacuum-tube' electronics? Do you have any electronic vacuum tubes in consumer equipment in your home?

8 Can you think of ways in which electronics is improving the motor car?

9 What type of electronic equipment has been left on the Moon's surface, and what kind of information is it sending back?

10 Why are some people worried about using computers to store personal information for, say, tax purposes or police records?

11 How are satellites helping to improve the accuracy of weather forecasting?

12 What types of electronic musical instrument do you know?

A2 SOURCES OF ELECTRICAL ENERGY

A2.1 Natural sources of energy

An absolutely essential requirement for the operation of electronic equipment in this Electronic Age is a dependable and safe power supply — the electrical energy which a lightning flash supplies is neither dependable nor safe!

In fact, there are no useful natural sources of electrical energy, so Man has to generate his own power from other natural forms of energy, such as the *fossil fuels* (coal, oil, and gas), *nuclear fuels* (uranium and plutonium), *gravitational energy* (tidal and falling water), the energy of *sunlight,* and *geothermal energy* (the Earth's internal store of heat). It is not the purpose in this course to describe the various engineering feats which have provided us with what, to many people, seems like an inexhaustible supply of electricity; however, you should be aware of the following facts:

a) It is not likely that either the Earth's internal store of heat or its gravitational energy will ever be 'tapped' on a large scale and be able to supply more than a very small fraction of the total electrical energy required in the future.

b) Coal has traditionally been the main source of heat for producing steam for driving the generators in coal-fired power stations — see fig. A2.1. However, as the sources of coal and other forms of fossil fuels become depleted,

Fig A2.1 A coal-fired power station. The CEGB's 2000 MW (million watts) station at Ratcliffe-on-Soar near Nottingham. *(Courtesy Central Electricity Generating Board)*

Fig. A2.2 This forerunner of nuclear power stations of the future is the Prototype Fast Reactor at Dounreay, Caithness, Scotland. *(Courtesy United Kingdom Atomic Energy Authority)*

nuclear energy is taking its place as the provider of the source of heat — see fig. A2.2.

c) Sunlight provides an almost unlimited source of energy, if only it could be tapped. The solar cell — see fig. A2.3 — has been developed to convert the energy of sunlight into electricity. However, there are as yet no large-scale power stations giving us electricity in this way. Cost, the fact that a large collecting area of solar cells is required, and the problem of cloudy days, let alone the darkness of night, are partly responsible, but artificial satellites and other 'space vehicles' do make use of the strong and almost unhindered sunlight in space — see fig. A2.4. It has even been suggested recently that large solar-power collecting stations should be constructed in space from solar cells and beam down the electrical energy on microwaves; but these suggestions are surely in the realm of science-fiction — or are they?

A2.2   Cells and batteries

Electronics project work of the type described in *Basic Electronics* requires reliable sources of electrical energy. These sources are known as *cells* or *batteries;* a battery consists of more than one cell. Fig. A2.5 shows a collection of dry batteries and cells. The three small 'button' cells are the type sold for hearing aids and cameras; they provide a voltage of about 1.4 volts and are suitable for some kinds of small-scale project work.

10

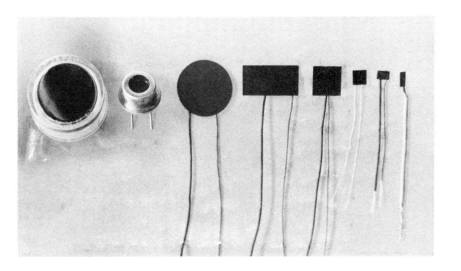

Fig. A2.3 A range of silicon solar-cells used for converting light energy into electrical energy approximately ¾ actual size. *(Courtesy Photain Controls Ltd)*

Fig. A2.4 Space stations, like this one called *Skylab* which was launched in 1973, use thousands of solar-cells making up the panels shown. This artist's impression shows an Apollo command module docked with the station. *(Courtesy USIS)*

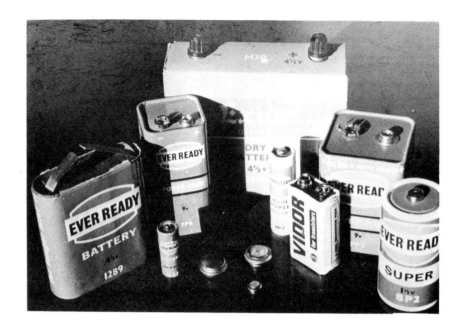

Fig. A2.5 A collection of dry cells and batteries.

Wet cells or batteries usually have a higher *current capacity* than dry cells; that is, they can supply a high current for a longer period than can a dry battery. A wet battery is used in a car for this reason, for it will operate a number of devices such as heater fan, wiper motor, starter motor, and lights, all requiring a high current. The car battery is a *lead–acid* type, but another type of wet battery is the NIFE *alkali type*. Both types of wet battery (or accumulator) can be recharged after they have run down – they 'accumulate' electrical energy. Electronic circuit projects for the car are usually designed to operate from 12 volts, but we shall find it more convenient to operate electronic circuits from a 9 volt battery of the type shown in fig. A2.5. This type consists of a layer of cells each of which provides a voltage of 1.5 volts, having the construction shown in fig. A2.6. See Section C for the meaning of 'volts' and 'amperes'.

A2.3 Two special types of cell
There are some types of electrical power sources which we are hearing more about these days. One is known as the *radioisotope thermoelectric generator,* and the other as the *fuel-cell.*

The radioisotope thermoelectric generator makes use of the heat generated by a radioactive isotope (usually plutonium) to produce a voltage at the join (or

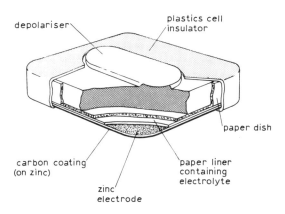

Fig. A2.6 The structure of a layer cell which makes up a 9 volt dry battery.

junction) between two different metals – see Section A3.1. These generators are already being used to operate electronic equipment for long periods in hostile and remote environments. For example, *buoys* now provide an automatic warning light and radio beacon to guide shipping through dangerous waters; a *heart pace-maker* can now be implanted in the body to give electrical impulses to stimulate the failing heart – see fig. A1.6; and in *space*, where instruments are required to operate in the depths of space, a long way from the Sun, these generators provide a reliable source of electrical energy.

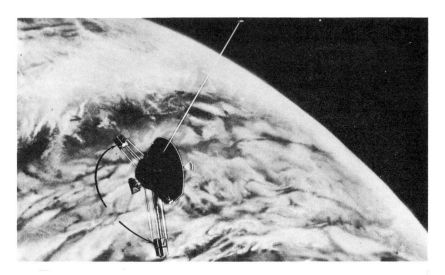

Fig. A2.7 An artist's impression of Pioneer 10 passing by the planet Jupiter. The radio-isotope thermoelectric generators are marked by arrows, and provide electrical energy even though the spacecraft is a long way from the sun. *(Courtesy USIS)*

The fuel-cell has been known to us for longer than the radioisotope thermo-electric generator — the first fuel-cell was made in 1839. One well-developed type uses oxygen and hydrogen as the fuels, and has already seen service in the Apollo flights to the Moon, but more development work seems to be required before fuel-cells are suitable for everyday use in the home or in electric cars. The principle of the hydrogen–oxygen fuel-cell is shown in fig. A2.8. Both these gases be-

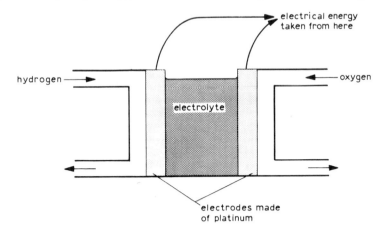

Fig. A2.8 The principle of a hydrogen-oxygen fuel cell.

come 'ionised' — see Section A7.5 — in the pores of the 'spongy' electrodes made from the rather costly metal platinum, and electrical energy is generated, while water is produced from the combination of hydrogen atoms with oxygen atoms. Fuel-cells are now being developed using fuels other than oxygen and hydrogen — it may even be possible to make a fuel-cell which will work from the fluids in the body, so that a heart pacemaker would never need to be removed from the body.

A3 EXPERIMENTS: GENERATING ELECTRICITY

A3.1 Electricity from heat

You will need two roughly equal lengths of wire of different metals, such as copper and iron, or copper and constantan (eureka). If the copper wire is enamelled, clean its ends before twisting one end of the iron, or constantan, wire with one end of the copper wire, as shown in fig. A3.1.

Next connect the free pair of ends to the terminals of a multimeter switched on a sensitive current range, say, 50 or 100 microamperes (see Section A3.5 for the meaning of 'micro'). Now warm the junction of the two metals – you may need to use a flame – and watch for the current flowing in the circuit. This is an example of a circuit in which heat is converted into electrical energy, but in this experiment only a very small amount of the heat in the flame is actually converted. The simple set-up of fig. A3.1 is known as a *thermocouple,* and is often used for measuring temperature. However, we are interested in it because it is the basis of a *radioisotope thermoelectric generator,* a use for which was mentioned in Section A2.3.

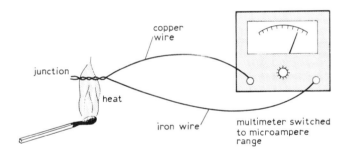

Fig. A3.1 Making heat produce electricity.

1 What do you notice about the direction of the current flowing in the circuit? Is it one-way current (called a 'direct current'), or does it regularly change direction (called an 'alternating current')?

A3.2 Electricity from chemicals

Soak a 4 cm square of blotting paper in vinegar or the juice of a lemon, and sandwich the paper between a 10p coin and a 2p coin (or coins of dissimilar metals). Press the leads from the multimeter switched to the 1 volt range (or higher) on the coins as shown in fig. A3.2. Notice the effect on the current flowing through the meter of interchanging the connections to the multimeter.

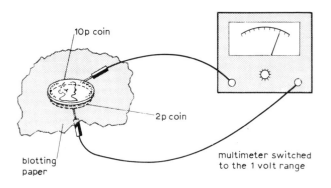

Fig. A3.2 Producing electricity from chemical action.

In this circuit, the chemical activity between the vinegar or the lemon juice (which are acidic liquids) and the metals of the coins produces electrical energy. Chemical cells based on this principle are the wet and dry cells mentioned in Section A2.2. All cells of this type have an *electrolyte* (vinegar or lemon juice in this case) and two *electrodes* (the two coins in your experiment).

1 What do you notice about the direction of the current flowing in the circuit? Is it a one-way current (called a 'direct current'), or does it regularly change direction (called an 'alternating current')?

A3.3 Electricity from magnetism

For this experiment you will need a small permanent magnet such as the bar type shown in fig. A3.3. A coil made from enamelled copper wire or other insulated wire must be wound on a 'former' such as a cardboard tube. About 30 turns of wire will be adequate, although you might need to increase this number if you have a weak magnet or a rather insensitive meter.

Fig. A3.3 shows how the coil is connected to a microammeter reading, say, to 100 microamperes (see Section A3.5). Move either the magnet or the coil, or both, and the needle of the multimeter will move, showing that electrical energy is being generated. In this case, although magnetism is absolutely essential for the experiment to work, magnetic energy is not being used up since, as you will see, the magnet does not get weaker. In fact, the energy comes from your own efforts, not that you will get tired in this experiment! More is said about this method of producing electrical energy in Section E.

This simple experiment illustrates how electricity is produced on a large-scale in nuclear, coal-fired, and hydroelectric power stations around the world. The turbines in these power stations are driven by steam or moving water, and, these in turn drive generators (the latter basically consisting of coils of wire rotating in magnetic fields).

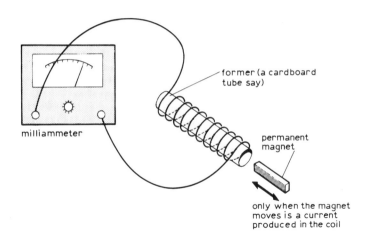

former (a cardboard tube say)

milliammeter

permanent magnet

only when the magnet moves is a current produced in the coil

Fig. A3.3 Making magnetism produce electricity.

1 Can you get current to flow in the circuit if neither the magnet nor the coil moves?

2 Is it possible to obtain alternating current (that is, current which regularly changes direction) from this circuit?

A3.4 Electricity from light

For this experiment you do not necessarily need a silicon solar-cell, since these are costly. *Selenium* solar-cells are cheaper, and these cells are usually about 60 mm diameter and 2 mm thick, and provide a current of about 10 milli-amperes (10/1000) A when light is shone onto their sensitive side. See Section A3.5 for an explanation of 'milli'.

Since it is difficult to make electrical contact with the sides of a selenium cell, you might use the idea shown in fig. A3.4 to mount the cells. This arrangement makes it easier to connect the selenium cells to, say, a 100 mA meter to see how changing the illumination affects the current produced. Note that two cells, connected in parallel − see Section A4.7 − are used here to increase the current available from the cells. In this circuit, light energy is being converted into electrical energy.

1 Is the current available from the solar-cell circuit a direct current or an alternating current?

A3.5 High and low values of current and voltage

In order to do the previous experiments, you will have needed to make use of a milliammeter or a microammeter, and you probably used a multimeter to obtain these scales. The words 'milli' and 'micro' are known as 'prefixes', since they are

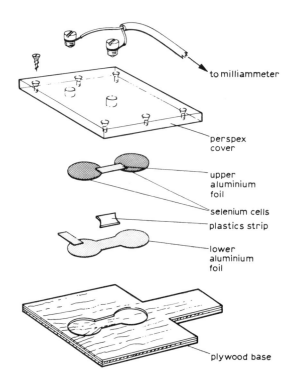

to milliammeter

perspex cover

upper aluminium foil

selenium cells

plastics strip

lower aluminium foil

plywood base

Fig. A3.4 One way of making contact with selenium cells.

fixed *before* a quantity like an ampere or a volt to indicate how small the quantity is to be. The prefix 'milli' means 'one thousandth of'. Therefore, a milliampere is (1/1000) of an ampere or (1/1000) A or 1 mA, the letter 'm' standing for 'milli'. Another way of writing (1/1000) A is 0.001 A. The prefix 'micro' means 'one millionth of'. Therefore, the microampere is (1/1 000 000) of an ampere or (1/1 000 000) A or 1 μA, the Greek letter 'μ' ('mu') standing for 'micro'. Another way of writing (1/1 000 000) A is 0.000 001 A.

There are fractions of quantities even smaller than 'milli' and 'micro'; for instance, you will meet the 'pico' and the 'nano' when referring to capacitor values in Section D.

As well as small currents, small values of voltage can be written in the same way. Thus 1 millivolt is written as 1 mV.

For quantities which are much greater than a few 'tens', we can prefix the quantity with 'kilo', meaning 'one thousand times', and 'mega', meaning 'one million times'. You will not be using kilovolts and kiloamperes in your study of electronics in this course, but kilohms and megohms are used for resistor values and are explained in Section C. In fact, you may have already noticed these quantities on the resistance scales of the multimeter you have been using.

A4 SIMPLE CIRCUITS

A4.1 Making electrons move

The experiments you carried out in Section A3 showed just four ways of producing electrical energy. Each experiment produced an electric current made up of electrons flowing through wires called electrical *conductors*. Electronics is concerned with putting these moving electrons to work in a useful way, such as lighting lamps, driving electric motors, switching circuits on and off, communicating, controlling, etc.

An electrical force is required to make electrons move. This force is known as an *electron-moving force,* often abbreviated to 'e.m.f.', and is measured in units of *volts*. In the experiments of the previous section, heat, light, and chemical action each set up an electron-moving force which forced electrons to move through the wires when a circuit was made. The flow of electrons is called an 'electric current' and is measured in units of *amperes*. Volts and amperes are related in a way you will learn about in Section C.

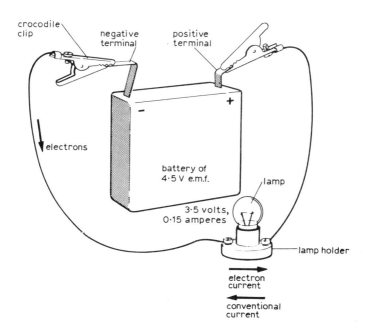

Fig. A4.1 A simple circuit.

A4.2 Making electrons light a lamp

Fig. A4.1 shows a simple arrangement in which an electron-moving force of 4.5 volts drives electrons through the electron-conducting wires and through the filament of the lamp.

The filament of the lamp is different from the wires of the rest of the circuit: it is a coiled coil of tungsten wire. In passing through this filament, electrons do work, and the heat they produce is sufficient to raise the temperature of the filament to about 1000 °C so that it emits light.

A4.3 Electron current and conventional current

Electrons flow from the negative terminal of a battery or cell to the positive terminal, as shown in fig. A4.1. This current is known as *electron current.* Electricity was once thought to flow from the positive terminal to the negative terminal of a battery, and, if an arrow is drawn showing current flowing in this 'wrong' direction, it is called *conventional current.* In the circuits which follow in this course, it is the conventional-current direction which is marked, unless the electron-current direction is clearly stated.

A4.4 A circuit diagram

Fig. A4.2 shows the electronic circuit of the arrangement of fig. A4.1. A circuit diagram uses *symbols* to show how electronic components are connected together. Note the abbreviations for volt (**V**) and ampere (**A**) and the symbols for the battery and for the lamp. The battery is made up of a number of cells — more than two — which is why dots are shown between the two cell symbols.

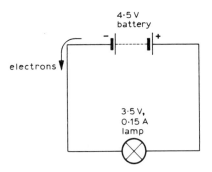

Fig. A4.2 A simple circuit diagram.

A4.5 Using an S-DeC to make a circuit

The plan view of an S-DeC is shown in fig. A4.3. By looking at an S-DeC you will notice that it consists of a box containing two panels of 'rails'. There are seven completely separate 'rails' in each panel.

20

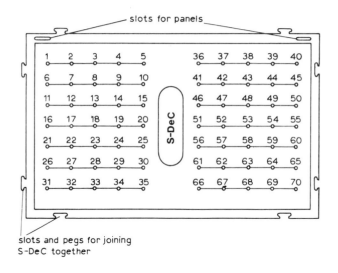

Fig. A4.3 A plan view of an S-DeC.

Each rail has five contacts to which components may be connected. Each contact is clearly numbered and, as you can see from fig. A4.3, contacts 1, 2, 3, 4, and 5 are connected together in the first rail; contacts 6, 7, 8, 9, and 10 form the second rail; etc. Components are connected together simply by pushing the wire into the appropriate hole – and insertion to a depth of about 10 millimetres (10 mm) is sufficient to enable the wire to be gripped by the phosphor-bronze clips. Sometimes you will find it necessary to make connections between rails,

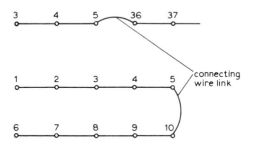

Fig. A4.4 Making links between rails on an S-DeC.

and for this purpose you will need some single-strand copper wire. This should preferably be PVC covered, bared for about 15 mm at each end, and just long enough to make a link between the rails. In addition, this wire should not be too thick nor too thin – about 16 s.w.g. wire is suitable. Fig. A4.4 shows how connections between rails may be made in two ways.

21

The circuits which follow show how an S-DeC is used to assemble components to make a circuit. On the S-DeC layout, a number is given where a component is to be plugged into the 'DeC'. All you have to do is to push the lead of the component into the appropriate socket. As a start, fig. A4.5 shows the S-DeC layout for the circuit of fig. A4.2.

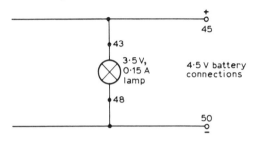

Fig. A4.5 S-DeC connections for the simple circuit of fig. 4.2.

A4.6   An S-DeC series circuit with lamps and a battery

Fig. A4.6(a) shows a practical circuit which you might set up to connect two lamps in *series* if you did not have an S-DeC. The meaning of the series connection is made clear if you look at fig. A4.6(b). It is obvious from this circuit that whatever current flows through lamp L_1 must also flow through lamp L_2. L_1 and L_2 are said to be '*in series*', meaning 'one-after-the-other'.

If you use an S-DeC, then one possible circuit layout is shown in fig. A4.6(c) Here each lamp is connected across a different pair of rails.

1   Do both lamps go out if connection 45 is broken?

2   Is it possible to break just one connection and make only one lamp go out?

3   Is the current which passes through L_1 the same as that passing through L_2?

It is important for you to notice that in this series circuit, if the current is prevented from flowing through one lamp, it is also prevented from flowing through the other lamps in series with it.

4   What do you notice about the brightness of the lamps in this series circuit compared with the simple circuit of fig. A4.5?

5   Use a wire link across holes 48 and 53. Why does lamp L_2 go out? Why has L_1 become brighter? Is the circuit now like that of fig. A4.2?

22

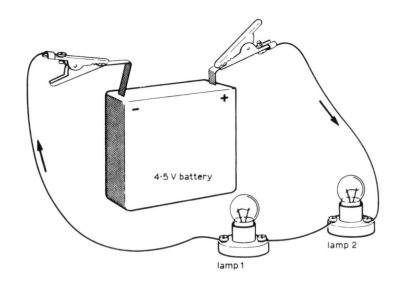

Fig. A4.6(a) How lamps are connected in series.

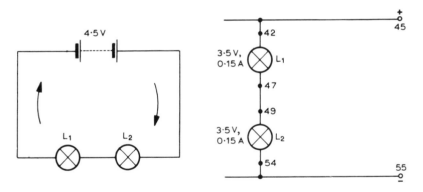

Fig. A4.6(b) Lamps connected in series.   Fig. A4.6(c) S-DeC connections for fig. 4.6(b).

A4.7 An S-DeC parallel circuit with lamps and a battery

Fig. A4.7(a) shows a practical circuit which you might set up to connect two lamps
in *parallel* if you did not have an S-DeC. The meaning of the parallel connection
is made clear if you look at fig. A4.7(b). The difference between this connection
and the series circuit is that the current from the battery divides, part flowing
through one lamp and part through the other. Thus 'parallel' means 'side-by-side'.

If you use an S-DeC, then one possible layout is shown in fig. A4.7(c). Here
each lamp is connected across the same pair of rails.

23

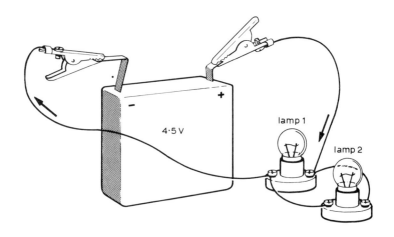

Fig. A4.7(a) How lamps are connected in parallel.

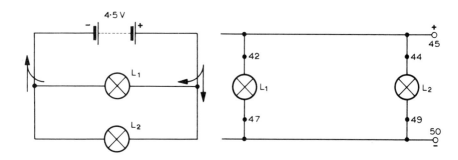

Fig. A4.7(b) Lamps connected in parallel. Fig. A4.7(c) S-DeC connections for fig. 4.7(b).

1 Disconnect the lamp at connection 42. Which lamp goes out?

2 Which connection would you break in order to make L_2 go out but not L_1?

3 Is the current flowing from the battery the same as the sum of the currents flowing through the lamps?

4 What do you notice about the brightness of the lamps compared with the simple circuit of fig. A4.5?

A4.8   An S-DeC series–parallel combination circuit

Fig. A4.8 shows a circuit consisting of one lamp in series with two other lamps connected in parallel. Set up this circuit on S-DeC, and carry out the following tests.

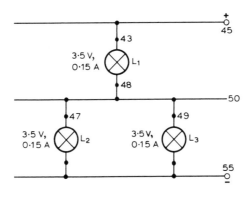

Fig. A4.8 Lamps connected in series and parallel.

1 Disconnect the wire from hole 48. Which lamp goes out? Why?

2 What other connections may be broken to put all the lamps out?

3 Which connection can you break to make just lamp L_2 go out?

4 Is it possible to make just lamp L_1 go out?

In a circuit of this type, the component in series with the parallel combination of components carries all of the current to the parallel components. Therefore, if the current is prevented from flowing through L_1, by breaking the connection at 48, all the lamps go out.

5 Use a wire link to 'short out' lamp L_3. Is L_1 as bright now as it was in fig. A4.5?

6 Short out lamp L_1. What happens to the brightness of lamps L_2 and L_3?

7 Draw a circuit diagram of fig. A4.8.

A4.9   The meaning of 'open' and 'closed' circuit

The words 'open circuit' and 'closed circuit' are used a lot in electronics and are really self-explanatory. A switch 'opens' a circuit when it is in the 'off' position, and 'closes' it when it is in the 'on' position. In the above S-DeC circuits, you made an open circuit when you broke an S-DeC connection. Thus 'open circuit' means 'breaking' the conducting path through which electrons flow, and 'closed circuit' means 'making' the conducting path through which electrons flow.

A5 USING SWITCHES

A5.1 The importance of switches

The commonest application for a switch is to switch electricity on and off. It is used as a safety device when switching off power if an accident happens, and it is used for economy reasons when conserving electrical power.

Switches also have a very active part to play in an electronic digital computer — see Section A1.4 — which is designed to perform thousands of switching operations per second. In the early computers, electromechanical switches like the *reed relay* and the *electromagnetic relay* were used — see Section A5.2. Nowadays electronic switches having no moving parts are used — the electronic calculator shown in fig. A1.3 uses such solid-state switches.

In Sections I and J you will find examples of how a transistor behaves as a solid-state switch. For the present, we shall see how some types of mechanical switch can be used.

A5.2 Types of mechanical switch

You will be using switches which require a mechanical force to operate them. The force brings together, or separates, electrically conducting metal contacts.

a) Push-button switch The switch shown in fig. A5.1 is a simple 'push-to-make, release-to-break' type. You now know what is meant by 'making' and 'breaking' an electrical connection from the simple experiments you carried out in Section A4.

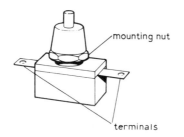

mounting nut

terminals

Fig. A5.1 An example of a push-button switch.

There are two symbols for this type of switch, depending upon whether pushing 'makes' or 'breaks' the contact — see fig. A5.2. A 'push-to-make, push-again-to-break', or 'push-push', switch is also available and is often used as a simple on–off switch for a table lamp. Another example of this kind of switch is the foot-controlled headlamp-dip-switch on a car.

1 Are there any other uses of push-button switches in your home?

Fig. A5.2 Circuit symbols for two types of push switch.

b) Slide switch and toggle switch   Fig. A5.3 shows the appearance of two common types of these switches. They are manufactured as either 'single pole, double throw' (s.p.d.t.) or 'double pole, double throw' (d.p.d.t), the circuit symbols for these types being shown in fig. A5.4. The 'poles' of a switch are the number of separate circuits the switch will make or break simultaneously. Thus the d.p.d.t. type will operate two separate circuits at the same time.

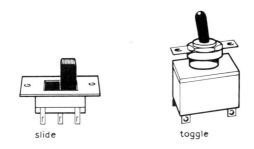

slide   toggle

Fig. A5.3 Example of a slide and a toggle switch.

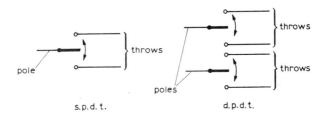

Fig. A5.4 S.p.d.t. and d.p.d.t. switch symbols.

The s.p.d.t. type is sometimes known as a 'change over' switch, since the pair of contacts which is 'made' changes over as the switch is operated. One common use for a s.p.d.t. switch is to operate a light from two different positions, the top and bottom of the stairs, for instance, as the following circuit shows.

1 Set up the S-DeC circuit of fig. A5.5. Use the wire links to show how the lamp may be switched on and off from the two positions A and B.

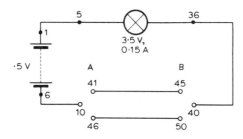

Fig. A5.5 S-DeC connections for a two-way switch.

c) Microswitch The main features of this switch are that only a small force is applied to operate it, and this force need act through only a small distance. In fig. A5.6, the microswitch is fitted with a lever making the force required even less, although this does mean that the force has to act through a larger distance.

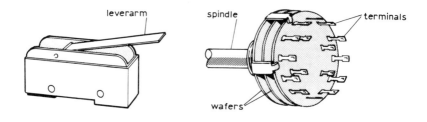

Fig. A5.6 One type of microswitch.   Fig. A5.7 A wafer rotary switch.

d) Wafer switch This is an example of a rotary switch, one type being shown in fig. A5.7. A number of paxolin discs (or wafers) carrying contacts are mounted on a spindle, so that a number of separate switching combinations can be made. 1 pole, 12 way (or 'throw'); 2 pole, 6 way; 3 pole, 4 way; 4 pole, 3 way; or 6 pole, 2 way switching are possible switching arrangements for a wafer switch.

e) Electromagnetic relay A small current through the coil shown in fig. A5.8 magnetises a bar of soft iron which is drawn to the coil and opens and closes the contacts. These contacts can be used to switch much larger currents than that flowing through the coil — hence the reason for using the word 'relay'. This type of switch is explained in more detail in Section E.

f) Reed switch This type consists of two reeds, made of ferromagnetic material — see fig. A5.9 — which are easily magnetised and demagnetised. The contacts are protected by being sealed in a glass envelope which contains an inert gas, such as nitrogen, to reduce corrosion of the contacts.

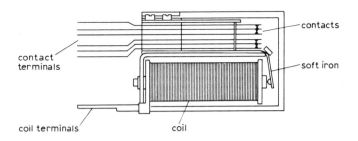

Fig. A5.8 An electromagnetic relay.

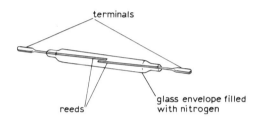

Fig. A5.9 A reed switch.

If a permanent magnet is brought close to the reeds, the reeds are magnetised, attract each other, and close. Remove the magnet, and the reeds open. Reed switches are also operated by being placed inside a coil of wire through which a current is passed – see Section E. Fig. A5.10 shows another type of reed switch known as a 'change-over' type. Can you see how it operates when a magnet is brought close to it?

Fig. A5.10 Change-over reed switch.

The reed switch has numerous applications, since it has the following advantages over other forms of switch.

i)   It is a 'proximity' switch, meaning that it is the nearness of the magnet which alone causes the reeds to close. This 'action at a distance' enables the switch to be operated through a shield, provided that the shield is not a material which can be magnetised.

ii) Since the contacts are sealed in an envelope, reed switches are ideal for use in atmospheres containing explosive gases. The sparking which occurs at the contacts of an unsealed switch could lead to an explosion.

29

iii) It is a fast switch; some types of reed switch can be operated 2000 times per minute.

iv) It has a long life. Up to 1000 million switching operations can be obtained from a reed switch, provided it is switching a low current. High currents rapidly cause deterioration of the contacts.

A5.3   Uses for a reed switch

a) Position control   The sketch in fig. A5.11 shows the principle employed here. The object being positioned carries a magnet, and the reed switch is fixed at the position at which the object is to stop. When the magnet is close to the reed switch, the reeds close, and this is arranged to switch off the power to the positioning motor. This application could be made use of in model-train control.

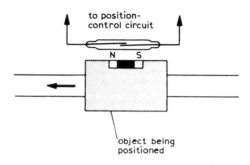

Fig. A5.11   Reed switch used for position control.

b) Measuring rotational speed   Fig. A5.12 shows how a rotating shaft, which is carrying a magnet, operates a fixed reed switch. The reed switch is a fast switch, so the shaft can rotate at up to 2000 rev/min and each rotation of the shaft will cause the reeds to close. The pulses from the reed switch can be used to give a 'rev/min' reading on the dial of a meter; the instrument obtained would then be called a *tachometer.*

c) Push-button switch   Fig. A5.13 shows how the movement of the magnet against the action of the spring causes the reeds to close. The magnet will be found to be nearer the reeds when they close than when they re-open. The difference in the two positions is caused by *magnetic hysteresis* — see Section E - in the ferromagnetic material of the reeds. This 'pull-in/pull-out differential' can be considerably reduced by using the arrangement shown in fig. A5.14. Two magnets are used with their opposite poles facing each other, one magnet being fixed and the other moveable.

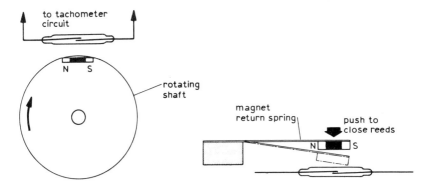

Fig. A5.12 Reed switch used for
measurement of rotational speed.

Fig. A5.13 Push-button switch using a reed switch.

This arrangement also enables a 'normally-open' reed switch to be operated as a 'normally-closed' type. You should experiment with these arrangements until you are quite clear how the simple two-reed switch can be used either to reduce the pull-in/pull-out differential or as a normally-closed switch.

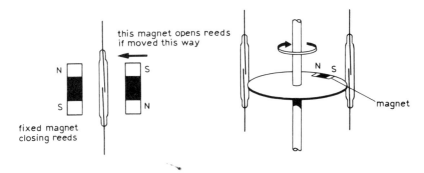

Fig. A5.14 How to reduce the pull-in pull-out
differential for a reed switch and how to
operate it as a normally-closed switch.

Fig. A5.15 How a rotary-position
indicator works.

d) Rotary-position indicator Fig. A5.15 shows the principle. A magnet on a rotating shaft closes the reeds of the nearest reed switch. This closed reed switch can be used to operate a lamp or sound an alarm, so that the position of the shaft can be found without actually seeing it. A weathercock could be designed making use of this idea. Four reed switches would give the four main points of the compass, but normally you would also want to record points like ENE. How many reed switches would you need for recording compass points such as ENE and SSE?

A6 CONSTRUCTIONAL PROJECTS

A6.1 Open-door alarm

This useful application of a reed switch gives a warning when a door is opened. As shown in fig. A6.1, a magnet is inset in the door (it can be made invisible), and the normally-open reed switch and the magnet closing the reeds are inset in the door-frame. The reed switch is connected to a lamp, bell, or buzzer. When the door is open, the fixed magnet closes the reeds so that the alarm will sound if the 'set-alarm' switch is closed. But when the door is closed, the magnet in the door cancels the effect of the fixed magnet, and the reeds open. This means that the set switch can be closed and the alarm will not sound. If now the door is opened, the reeds close under the action of the magnet, and the alarm is operated. An extension of this idea which uses an electronic circuit is described in Section J. A normally-closed reed switch simplifies the circuit.

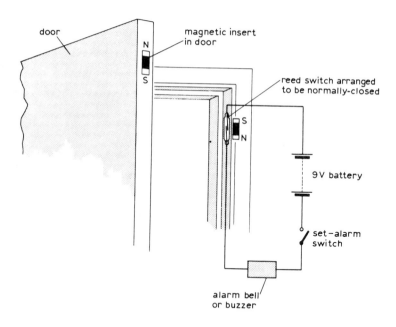

Fig. A6.1 The arrangement required for a door-alarm circuit.

A6.2 Building a carbon microphone

Microphones are essential for telephone and radio communications, since they convert the sound waves into electrical signals for communicating by wire or over the air. At the receiving end of the communications link, these signals are converted back into sound waves by means of an earpiece or a loudspeaker.

There are many different types of microphone, and the carbon microphone is not the most sensitive, but the one described here is very easy to construct provided you have a little patience and can find a source of scrap metal and other materials.

Construction

A circular box (wood, plastics, or cardboard) is required, about 70 millimetres (mm) inside diameter and 25 mm deep. Into the removable 'top' of this box, a hole about 20 mm in diameter is cut or drilled. Into this hole is fitted a tinplate cone to 'collect' the sound waves. This cone might be made from plate cut as shown in fig. A6.2.

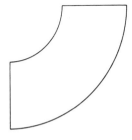

Fig. A6.2 The shape of the tinplate or aluminium sheet required for the cone.

Two carbon rods are needed; those from two dry cells (e.g. EverReady SP2) are suitable. Two pieces, complete with a brass end-cap, are cut to lengths 10 mm and 20 mm. To each brass cap, solder two 50 mm lengths of insulated copper wire (preferably of the flexible, multistrand type). You must ensure that one piece of wire is soldered to the side of one end-cap. The longer of the two rods is pushed through a hole in the base, as shown in fig. A6.3, making a tight fit. A paper tube, about 20 mm long and 12 mm diameter, is then glued in place so that each carbon rod lies along its axis.

The unused pieces of rod are broken up into smaller pieces and 'tumbled' to round them off. The dust is discarded, so that you are left with granules of carbon about 1 mm in diameter. Sufficient granules are placed in the paper tube to fill it. The top of the tube is sealed with fluffed-up cotton wool.

The diaphragm, made from flat shim steel about 0.075 mm thick, is cut to fit the box and is supported around the edge. The diaphragm should not make contact with the top of the cardboard tube or with the cone. Its vibrations are transmitted to the carbon granules by means of the shorter carbon rod. The brass-rod end of the shorter rod is filed flat and is glued to the centre of the diaphragm so that it passes through the cotton wool into the carbon granules.

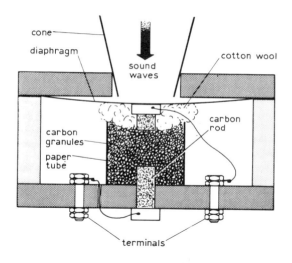

Fig. A6.3 A section through the carbon microphone.

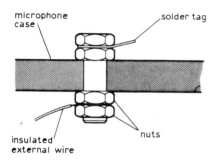

Fig. A6.4 The details of a terminal connection.

The two free ends of the leads are soldered to soldering tags as shown in fig.·
A6.4. These tags are bolted to the case of the microphone so that external connections to the two carbon rods can be made.

Use

A telephone earpiece is a suitable receiver for the electrical signals produced by
the microphone. This earpiece must be connected in series with the microphone
and with a battery of at least 4.5 V. A magnetic earpiece of the type supplied with
many transistor radios, or a loudspeaker, should also be tried. The following ad-
justments should be made to the circuit.

   1 Vary the e.m.f. of the battery so that the best results are obtained. Do not
      use too high an e.m.f., otherwise the loudspeaker may be damaged.

2 You may find that the microphone works better when placed horizontally rather than vertically. Try it in both positions.

3 Use insulated copper wire for external connections; conversation over long distances is possible.

4 Try using different-sized carbon granules or different diaphragm materials and thicknesses. Two circuits like the one shown in fig. A6.5 would form a two-way link.

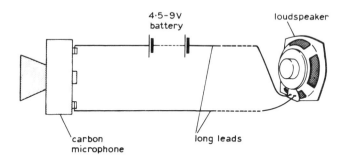

Fig. A6.5 A simple communications link using the microphone and a moving-coil loudspeaker.

The following is a brief explanation of the operation of this simple communications circuit.

The diaphragm of the microphone vibrates in unison with the sound waves which it receives. These vibrations cause changes in the resistance between the terminals of the microphone, since the diaphragm presses on the carbon granules and varies their spacing. These resistance changes cause changes in the current in the circuit, and in turn cause the diaphragm of the loudspeaker to move in unison with the current changes. Thus the loudspeaker reproduces the sound waves which were picked up by the microphone.

A6.3 Dry-battery charger

As you probably know, dry batteries in torches and transistor radios can be given a new lease of life if they are rested in a warm, dry place. However, instead of just leaving them idle, you can give them a charge. They are not intended to be charged like a car battery – see Section A2.2 – but it is surprising how good a run-down dry battery can become.

For this project you will need a low-voltage (12 volts) alternating-current supply from a standard a.c. supply unit. If one of these units is not available, you will need to 'house' a low-voltage mains transformer in a box to protect you from touching any bare mains connections.

Warning!

If you have no experience of wiring up circuits from the mains, find someone who has this experience to help you. The 240 volt a.c. mains voltage
is dangerous.

If the box is made of metal, it should be earthed by means of the earth line of
standard three-core cable, which is coloured green or green with a yellow stripe.

In the circuit of the dry-battery charger shown in fig. A6.6, make sure that the
line (brown, or red) and neutral (blue) wires from the mains plug cannot be
touched after the transformer has been 'housed'.

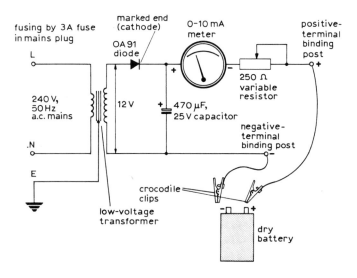

Fig. A6.6 Circuit diagram for the dry-battery charger.

You will see how the diode in the circuit works when you come to Section F,
but make sure it is connected as shown in the figure. The meter, the milliammeter
scale of a multimeter for instance, records the charging current. The rheostat ad-
justs the charging current, which should not exceed 5 mA. Stop charging when
the battery begins to warm up. Always connect the positive output connection
from the circuit to the positive terminal of the battery. With this charging circuit
you cannot charge dry batteries having an e.m.f. greater than 9 volts.

External connections to the battery can be made by using two terminal binding
posts. Be careful not to short the two leads from the charger unit, otherwise the
diode will fuse. To avoid this possibility, you should always set the variable
resistor to its maximum value before connecting the leads to the battery, and
then decrease this resistance to obtain the correct charging current of 5 mA.

A6.4 Building a low-voltage d.c. power supply

Introduction

The circuit shown in fig. A6.7 enables a mains-operated unit to be built which provides a voltage of about 9 V at a maximum current of 2 A for replacing dry batteries in the experiments and projects described in *Basic Electronics*.

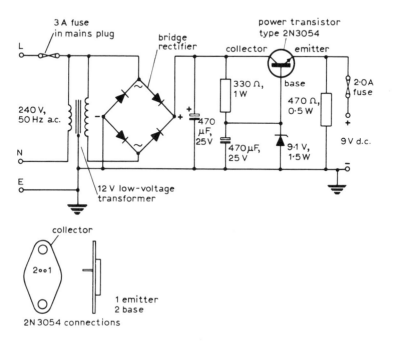

Fig. A6.7 Circuit diagram of a 9 volt stabilised d.c. supply.

Power supplies which are suitable for replacing dry batteries may be bought, of course; however, these are often expensive, since they provide a highly stabilised voltage for use with certain types of integrated circuit and transistor circuits, and such a high degree of stabilisation is unnecessary for the experiments and projects in *Basic Electronics*.

The unit shown in fig. A6.8 is based on the circuit of fig. A6.7 and can be built for about five pounds, the final cost being dependent upon what scrap or second-hand materials you have to hand.

Construction notes

a) Connection to the mains via a three-pin plug should not be made until the circuit has been assembled in a suitable box, and then this should not be done

Fig. A6.8 The circuit of the low-voltage power supply ready for assembly in a cabinet.

without the help of someone who has experience of handling mains-operated equipment.

b) The circuit for the unit shown in fig. A6.8 was soldered onto tagstrip. The transistor was mounted on a special heat-sink to dissipate the heat developed in the transistor when current is drawn from the circuit.

c) The operation of this transistor-stabilised circuit is described in Section J.

d) The metal case of the transformer must be earthed as indicated in fig. A6.7, as also should be the aluminium chassis (if one is used) on which the components are mounted.

A7 SOME IDEAS ABOUT ATOMS

A7.1 Where electrons come from

Since electronics is concerned with what electrons can usefully do, you should be able to say what part electrons play in the make-up of materials.

Nearly all materials on Earth are in solid, liquid, or gaseous form; but, whatever form these materials take, they all consist of atoms. *Electrons* are an important part of an atom, but so are *neutrons* and *protons;* and these are the three main particles from which atoms are made.

A7.2 The structure of an atom

Atoms are extremely small 'bits' of material – millions of them lie side-by-side across the diameter of this ink dot. Nevertheless, they can be seen, or at least their general position can be made out, as fig. A7.1 shows.

Although atoms are so small, a great deal is known about them; for instance, how they combine with one another to produce molecules, and what makes some atoms stable and some unstable.

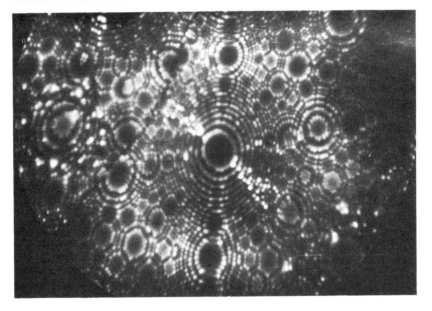

Fig. A7.1 A field-ion microscope produced this picture showing how atoms are arranged in a solid. Each circular area is caused by the presence of one atom. *(Courtesy Professor E. W. Mueller)*

It is not an easy matter to break an atom into pieces, or even to build one up out of protons, neutrons, and electrons. However, the fact that radioactive materials exist in us and around us proves that some atoms are naturally unstable and are breaking up of their own accord.

Uranium is a *radioactive* material, and atoms of it are all the time breaking up and changing into other types of atom. When a large number of uranium atoms are deliberately encouraged to break up, as in the nuclear reactor of a nuclear power station — see fig. A2.2 — a great deal of heat is produced which is used to generate electricity.

All atoms have a *nucleus*. It is the nucleus which changes when an atom is radioactive. The proton and the neutron have their home in the nucleus, but the electron is to be found outside the nucleus, making up what is called an 'electron cloud'. The nucleus is very small compared with the general size of an atom — say, the size of an orange compared with the vast volume of an English cathedral. Using this model for an atom, you can imagine the electrons themselves to be a swarm of flies in the cathedral.

Most of the mass of an atom lies in the nucleus. In fact, the proton and the neutron have about equal masses, but the electron has a mass about 2000 times
△ smaller than either of these.

▽ **A7.3   The electrical charge on neutrons, protons, and electrons**

The most important property of these three particles, from the point of view of our study of electronics, is their *electrical charge*.

The electron carries a negative charge and the proton a positive charge. These charges are equal in size but electrically opposite. Since the charges are opposite, electrons and protons attract each other. It is this attraction which keeps electrons in a cloud around the nucleus, although they don't actually fall into it. Each electron in an atom can possess only a certain value of energy, and the electrons arrange themselves into *shells* according to the energy they possess. Thus, each shell contains electrons of a particular energy.

The neutron does not carry any electrical charge — as you might expect, it is neutral. Although neutrons do not have any part to play in keeping the electrons in their shells, they are an important part of an atom since they contribute to the mass of an atom. But it is the number of protons which determines the type of
△ material to which the atom belongs, not the number of neutrons.

▽ **A7.4   The structure of hydrogen and oxygen atoms**

Hydrogen and oxygen are two very common elements, since their atoms go to make up that very useful and vital liquid called water. Actually, a hydrogen atom has the simplest structure of all. Fig. A7.2 shows two kinds of hydrogen atom to be found in nature, known as *'hydrogen-1'* and *'hydrogen-2'*. These two types are called *isotopes* of hydrogen. Water made from hydrogen-2 (also called

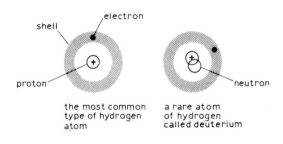

the most common type of hydrogen atom

a rare atom of hydrogen called deuterium

Fig. A7.2 Two kinds of hydrogen atom.

deuterium') is chemically the same as ordinary water, and you can drink it, grow plants in it, and swim in it. But it is slightly heavier than ordinary water, and water made from it is called *'heavy water'*. Heavy water also boils at a little higher than 100 °C and freezes at a little higher than 0 °C. Natural water contains a very small quantity of this heavy water. Note that both these kinds of hydrogen have an equal number of protons (one) in the nucleus, and it is this number which tells us that the atom belongs to the element called hydrogen.

The atom of oxygen is more complex than that of hydrogen. It has eight protons in its nucleus, but it can have seven, eight, or nine neutrons within it without changing the chemical properties of the atom. Fig. A7.3 shows the structure of the most common type of oxygen atom, having eight protons and eight neutrons in the nucleus. Eight electrons make up the normal oxygen atom, and they are arranged in two shells.

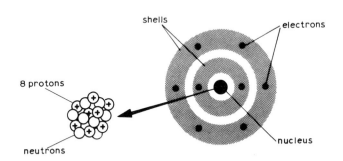

Fig. A7.3 The structure of an oxygen atom.

Atoms which have equal numbers of protons in their nuclei but different numbers of neutrons are known as *'isotopes'* of that element. You may have heard of radioactive isotopes in connection with their use in medicine, agriculture, and industry. One of the most important points for you to note is that in a normal atom (that is, a neutral atom), the number of electrons in the outer shells around the nucleus is equal to the number of protons in the nucleus. Atoms which have lost some electrons are known as *'ionised' atoms*.

1 The table shown in fig. A7.4 lists a few kinds of atom, some of which you will meet in this course. Can you fill in the blank spaces?

Atom	Number of protons in the nucleus	Number of electrons in the shells	Number of neutrons in the nucleus	Number of protons and neutrons in the nucleus
Hydrogen–1	1	1	0	1
Hydrogen–2	1	1	1	2
Oxygen–16	8	8	8	16
Oxygen–18	8	–	10	18
Copper–63	29	29	–	63
Silver–108	–	47	–	108
Silicon–28	–	–	14	28
Germanium–74	32	–	–	–
Carbon–12	–	6	–	–
Carbon–14	–	–	–	–
Iron–56	26	–	–	–

△   Fig. A7.4 Some information about atoms.

▽ **A7.5   Free electrons**

Protons and neutrons are bound together very tightly in the nucleus, despite the fact that neutrons have no electrical charge. There is a very powerful close-range force which acts between a neutron and a proton. The strength of this *nuclear* force accounts for the large quantities of energy generated when the nuclei of uranium atoms split apart in an atomic fission bomb or a nuclear reactor.

However, the force between an electron in one of the shells and the protons in the nucleus is much weaker than the nuclear forces – it is upon this weakness that electronics is based. An electrical current is caused by the movement of electrons. So weakly are some of the electrons bound to the atoms of silver and copper (two electrical conductors), that these electrons are called *'free' electrons*. However, for other materials (the electrical insulators), the electrons are less easily pushed around; they are more strongly bound to the atoms of insulators. Atoms which have more or less electrons than normal are called *'ionised' atoms*.

Although an electron will gladly settle down into one of the shells of an atom if there is place for it, in the emptiness of space, electrons are found moving vast distances without coming near enough to nuclei to form a neutral atom. Nearer home, we find electrons existing for a short time separate from a nucleus in a TV picture tube. The picture on the screen is 'written' by a fast-moving stream of electrons, as is the trace which is seen on the screen of an oscilloscope.

1   Why is there very little air in a TV or oscilloscope tube?

2   What other devices do you know which make use of free electrons moving in a vacuum?

3   What do you think happens to the electrons as soon as they strike the screen of a TV tube?

4   Can you name three electrical conductors (other than copper and silver) and three electrical insulators?

ANSWERS TO QUESTIONS – Section A

3.1.1 There is a one-way current direction for this circuit, so the heat develops a direct current.

3.2.1 This produces a direct current.

3.3.1 No. Either the magnet, the coil, or both must move – see Section E for more detail.

3.3.2 Yes, by continuously rotating the coil – see Section E for more detail.

3.4.1 Always direct current.

4.6.1 Yes. This is breaking a battery connection.

4.6.2 No. The same current flows through each lamp.

4.6.3 Yes.

4.6.4 They are less bright, since the current flowing from the battery is smaller.

4.6.5 Lamp L_2 has been 'shorted out' by the wire. Electric current flows more easily through this wire than through the bulb. Lamp L_1 now becomes brighter, since the current does not have to force itself through L_2 as well. The circuit is now like that of fig. A4.2.

4.7.1 Only lamp L_1, since L_2 is still connected across the battery.

4.7.2 Connection at contact 44 or 49.

4.7.3 If you add up the currents through L_1 and L_2, this equals the current flowing from the battery.

4.7.4 Slightly less bright perhaps, but roughly the same current is flowing through each lamp as in fig. A4.5.

4.8.1 All lamps go out, since this connection carries all the current to the lamps.

4.8.2 Connection at contact 43, 45, or 55.

4.8.3 Contacts at 47 or 52.

4.8.4 No, since this lamp also carries the current to the other lamps.

4.8.5 Shorting out L_3 also shorts out L_2, so the circuit is like that of fig. A4.5 and the lamp L_1 becomes as bright as that in fig. A4.5.

4.8.6 L_2 and L_3 become brighter.

4.8.7

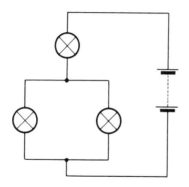

7.4.1

Oxygen-18	8	8	10	18
Copper-63	29	29	34	63
Silver-108	47	47	61	108
Silicon-28	14	14	14	28
Germanium-74	32	32	40	74
Carbon-12	6	6	6	12
Carbon-14	6	6	8	14
Iron-56	26	26	30	56

REVISION QUESTIONS — Section A

1 Electronic collars are being fitted to migrating animals so that space satellites can relay information to the ground about the movement of the animals. Do you think that experiments like this should be allowed?

2 How does electronics help the policeman do a better job?

3 How are nurses and doctors helped by electronics to carry out their work of looking after patients in hospitals?

4 Name four sources of energy which can be converted into electricity.

5 What is the meaning of the abbreviation 'e.m.f.'?

6 Electron-moving force is measured in units of . . . .
   heat? / volts? / amperes?

7 Electrical current is measured in units of . . . .
   light? / magnetism? / amperes?

8 A tungsten-filament lamp is intended to convert electrical energy into . . . .
   heat? / light? / magnetism?

9 Electrons flow from the negative terminal of a battery to the positive terminal.
   True? / False?

10 Conventional current flows in the . . . . direction to electron current in a circuit.
   same? / reverse?

11 The purpose of the S-DeC assembly is to build permanent circuits.
   True?/False?

12 When two lamps are connected in series, the current through one lamp . . . . the current through the other lamp.
   differs from? / equals?

13 When two lamps are connected in parallel, the current flow through one lamp also flows through the other lamp.
   True? / False?

14 Draw a circuit containing a battery and three lamps in series with each other.

15 Look at the circuit shown. How would you describe this circuit?

   Which lamp is brightest? Why?

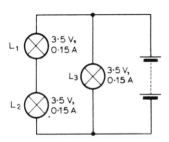

16 Name three types of mechanical switch.

17 What types of switches are used in present-day computers and calculating machines?

18 The main advantage of a reed switch is that the switch contacts can be touched and examined.

   True? / False?

19 The reed switch is operated by . . . .

   heat? / noise? / magnetism?

20 If correctly operated, a reed switch will perform millions of switching operations before it becomes unreliable.

   True? / False?

21 Name three uses for a reed switch.

22 Draw a circuit diagram for switching a light on and off from the top and bottom of a stairway. What type of switches are required for this application?

23 Two students each have a switch. Draw a circuit diagram which will enable a warning lamp to flash on when either student presses his switch.

24 What changes would you make to the circuit of question 23 if the light is to come on only when both students press their switch?

25 A rocket being prepared for launching has two men in it, each of whom has a two-position switch, one position marked 'hold' and one marked 'go'.

   Draw a circuit so that:

   a) a 'hold' light comes on when one has his switch in the 'hold' position;

   b) a 'go' light comes on only if both men have their switch in the 'go' position.

26 Electrons . . . . present in all materials on earth.

   are? / are not?

27 What is happening to an atom when it is radioactive?

28 The nucleus of an atom is a very small part of the space in an atom.

True? / False?

29 Electrons are held in the shells of an atom by a . . . . force which exists between these electrons and the protons in the nucleus.

magnetic? / electrical? / slow?

30 A hydrogen atom has . . . . protons in its nucleus.

one? / two? / no?

31 How does deuterium differ from hydrogen? How is it similar to hydrogen?

32 Draw a normal oxygen atom, showing the number of neutrons, protons, and electrons in its structure.

33 A carbon-12 atom has six protons in its nucleus. How many electrons and neutrons make up a normal carbon-12 atom?

34 Electrons can easily be removed from the atoms of materials which are electrical conductors.

True? / False?

35 When electrons are removed from the shells of an atom, the atom is said to be in a . . . . state.

unfortunate? / light? / ionised?

REVISION ANSWERS – Section A

4 Tidal (gravitational energy), coal and oil (fossil energy – chemical), uranium (nuclear energy), sunlight (solar energy)

5 Electron-moving force or, sometimes, electro-motive force

6 Volts

7 Amperes

8 Light is intended, but heat is produced too.

9 True

10 Reverse

11 False – it builds temporary circuits.

12 Equals

13 False

14

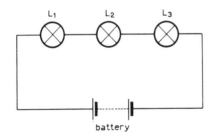

battery

15 The circuit consists of two identical series-connected lamps (L_1 and L_2) connected in parallel with another lamp identical to these two.

16 Slide switch, push-button switch, toggle switch

17 Solid-state switches having no moving parts

18 False – the reed switch is sealed to protect it from dust and handling.

19 Magnetism

20 True

21 See Section A5.3.

22 See fig. A5.5. s.p.d.t. types.

23 A parallel-connected circuit is required, as the figure shows. Push-to-make switches are used.

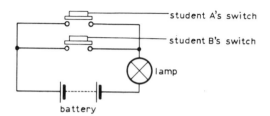

24 A series-connected circuit, as the figure shows:

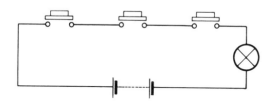

25 The circuit shown in the figure would be required. Note that it uses s.p.d.t. switches. The 'go' lamp can go on only when each switch is set in the 'go' position, but the 'hold' light comes on when either of the men has switched to the 'hold' position. The 'go' lamp is on in the circuit shown.

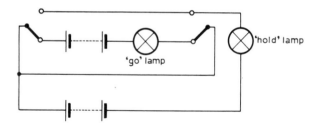

26 Are

27 The nucleus of the atom is breaking up.

28 True

29 Electrical

30 One

31 In addition to one proton in its nucleus, it also has one neutron. It is similar because it has one proton in its nucleus.

32 See fig. A7.3.

33 Six electrons and six neutrons

34 True

35 Ionised·

Section B
Measuring Instruments

B1 INTRODUCTION

B1.1 Three important instruments

In this section, a description is given of three important instruments — the *oscilloscope,* the *signal generator,* and the *multimeter.* The construction of a multimeter is outlined in Section G, but similar details for the oscilloscope and signal generator are not given.

B1.2 Why use electronic instruments?

A circuit can be assembled without an instrument to help you. But suppose, having built a circuit to produce, say, a warning note when light falls on a photo-cell, you find that the circuit does not work. What do you do? You might start by replacing some of the components by similar types, hoping that one of them is faulty and can be changed in this way. This is fault-finding by 'trial and error'. You might be lucky to correct the fault, but the procedure is time-consuming, and components are easily damaged — and you don't learn electronics properly this way. The use of instruments would help. They could tell you whether the battery was in a charged state; or whether a wire has a break in it; or whether the photo-cell is responding to light changes; or whether the transistor you are using is the correct type.

B1.3 The difference between a.c. and d.c.

The oscilloscope and multimeter measure alternating current (a.c.) or direct current (d.c.) currents and voltages. You must be quite clear as to the difference between a.c. and d.c.

Whereas d.c. voltages are always in the same sense or direction in a circuit, alternating voltages and currents regularly reverse their direction. As you noted in Section A, a battery produces a one-way or d.c. voltage across its terminals, and

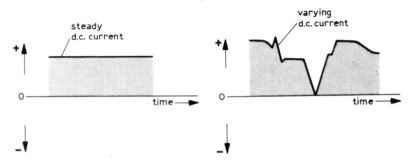

Fig. B1.1 Graph of a steady direct current. Fig. B1.2 Graph of a varying direct current.

the current this produces always flows in one direction through a d.c. circuit. A steady direct current is shown graphically in fig. B1.1. As time passes, the current remains at a steady level and in the same direction. Of course, the current will eventually fall to zero in the final stages of the battery's life, but during its whole life the current is still d.c. The plus and minus signs are used to indicate the two possible directions of current flow through the circuit.

1 Is the current graph shown in fig. B1.2 that of a d.c. or an a.c. change during the time considered?

B1.4 The frequency and period of alternating current

An alternating current is shown in fig. B1.3. The current is first in one direction and then in the reverse direction, but notice that there is a smooth change of current from zero to a maximum in one direction and then to zero once again. It smoothly increases to a maximum in the opposite direction and then to zero again before repeating the cycle. This is the variation of current obtained from the mains supply, and is known as a *'sinusoidal' variation,* since the variation is a *sine wave.* The terminals A and B in fig. B1.3 (marked + and −) show the change of polarity which occurs during each half cycle of the alternating current. It is this regular change of voltage which causes a corresponding regular change of current in an a.c. mains circuit.

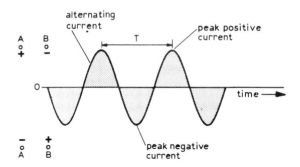

Fig. B1.3 Graph of a sinusoidal alternating current.

The time taken for the voltage at one terminal of the mains to change from its maximum positive value to its maximum negative value, and then back to its maximum positive value, is known as the *'period'* of the sine wave. For the a.c. mains voltage, the period T is 1/50 of a second:

$T = 1/50 = 0.02$ second

The number of complete periods of the sine wave in one second is known as the 'frequency' (f) of the a.c. mains voltage, and is given by

$f = 1/T = 50$ hertz (50 Hz)

Note: The hertz now replaces the cycle per second (c/s) as the unit for the frequency of all periodic changes, including a.c. mains voltage.

The frequency of the mains supply very rarely differs from 50 Hz, and it is therefore used as a frequency standard. In fact, some equipment, a mains-operated clock for instance, depends for its accuracy on the steadiness of this frequency.

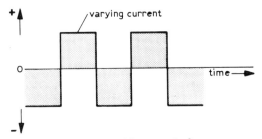

Fig. B1.4 Is this a.c. or d.c.?

1 Are the current changes shown in fig. B1.4 those of a.c. or d.c.?

2 What is the time occupied by one cycle of a radio wave of frequency 200 kHz?

The effect of the constantly reversing voltage, and hence current, is often noted when using mains-operated equipment. You might notice a flicker from fluorescent tube lighting – the trick is not to look directly at the tube but to see it 'out of the corner of your eye'. Sometimes a 100 Hz 'hum' is heard from an oven when it is switched on. And occasionally a 100 Hz hum may be heard from a mains radio, expecially if the radio is not of particularly good quality.

1 Why is the flicker or hum at a frequency of 100 Hz, not 50 Hz?

B1.5 Root-mean-square (r.m.s.) values of sinusoidal voltages

This description of an a.c. voltage or current often gives people difficulty. When we say that the voltage of the a.c. mains is 240 V, we mean that its *effective value* is 240 V. This figure is known as the r.m.s. voltage of the mains voltage and is the voltage which would give the same heating effect as a d.c. voltage of 240 V. However, the *maximum voltage* reached twice each period (see fig. B1.5) is higher than 240 V. The root-mean-square voltage is related to the peak voltage V_{max} by the equation

$$V_{rms} = V_{max}/\sqrt{2} \quad \text{or} \quad 0.7\, V_{max}$$

The relationship between V_{max} and V_{rms} is shown in fig. B1.5. It is easy to show that the peak voltage of the mains is about 340 V. From the above equation

$$V_{max} = V_{rms}/0.7 = 240/0.7 = 340\,\text{V}$$

54

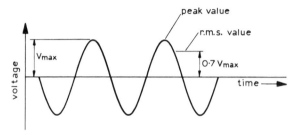

Fig. B1.5 Meaning of peak and r.m.s. voltage.

1 Calculate the r.m.s. value of a sinusoidally varying current which has a peak
value of 3 amperes (3A).

The answer is 2.1 A and means that a direct current of 2.1 amperes would give
the same heating effect as an alternating current whose peak value is 3 amperes.

B1.6 The importance of the earth connection

You know that the common method of connecting equipment to the mains is via
a three-pin plug of the type shown in fig. B1.6. Two pins are known as the *neutral*
and *line* pins, and the third and thicker pin is the *earth* pin. The earth pin connects
through the socket to the earth wire, which in turn is actually connected to the

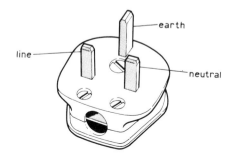

Fig. B1.6 The pins of a mains plug.

Fig. B1.7 Earth symbol.

earth or ground outside a building. The symbol for an earth connection is shown
in fig. B1.7. The neutral wire is also connected to ground at the generating station,
but actually a small voltage is often found to exist between the earth and the
neutral pins. This small voltage is caused by currents which flow through the
neutral wire from a number of items of equipment on the circuit. However, the
live wire carries a high voltage (240 V r.m.s) with respect to the neutral and the
earth wires. It is across the earth and line wires that a voltage variation of the type
shown in fig. B1.5 is obtained.

The earth connection is used for safety reasons. The metal case of an oscilloscope, or a soldering iron, or a washing machine could become 'live' if only the live and neutral connections are made, as shown in fig. B1.8. This would mean that a person touching the metal case and also having a good contact with ground would make a fairly good conducting path to ground. Sufficient current to kill him might flow through his body.

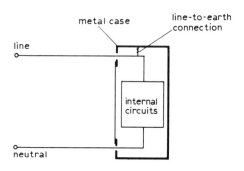

Fig. B1.8 The danger of not having an earth connection.

However, if the metal case is connected to ground — that is, earthed — and a fault occurs so that the line wire makes contact with the case, the fuse 'blows' because of the large current which flows through it. Thus the case cannot remain live, since the fuse blows first. The correct connections for the fuse and the earth are shown in fig. B1.9.

When a new plug is fitted to a piece of equipment, always make sure that the line, neutral, and earth wires are connected correctly. There is a new *colour code* for these three wires: brown for the line, blue for the neutral, and green and yellow stripe for the earth. This colour code replaces the older code of red, black, and green, respectively

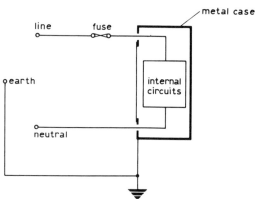

Fig. B1.9 How an earth connection is made.

B2.1   General description

The cathode-ray oscilloscope, CRO, enables voltage changes to be seen and measured. It can also be used to measure time and frequency.

The face of a typical oscilloscope is shown in fig. B2.1. Compare this with the one you have in the laboratory or workshop and try to identify the control knobs.

Fig. B2.1 The screen and control panel of a typical oscilloscope: Telequipment S51E. *(Courtesy Tektronix UK Ltd)*

The best way of finding out what an oscilloscope will do is to try out the controls one by one. You will find this easy on a simple instrument, and, once you have mastered it, you will find that a complex instrument can be operated almost as easily, since the basic features of CRO's are similar. The inner workings of the oscilloscope will not be studied, so make no attempt to probe about with the internal circuits unless you know what you are doing — some of the circuits carry lethally high voltages!

B2.2 How to obtain a spot on the screen of the oscilloscope

a) Set the FOCUS and BRIGHTNESS (or BRILLIANCE) controls to about mid-scale, and switch the TIME/CM or TIME-BASE to the OFF position.

b) Set the INPUT (or Y-SENSITIVITY or VOLTS/CM) control to about 5 V/cm
Set the TRIGGER LEVEL to AUTO or INTERNAL.

c) If a control with a position marked TV is fitted, switch it to NORMAL.

d) Switch on the mains supply and allow the instrument to warm up. A green or blue blob should appear on the screen. If it does not, you will be able to find it by rotating the Y-SHIFT and X-SHIFT controls. Focus the spot. A control marked ASTIG will help, if one is fitted. Do not allow the spot to remain stationary for any length of time at full brightness, or a 'burn' mark might be left on the screen.

e) The spot you have obtained is caused by a beam of electrons emitted from a hot filament in the CRO striking the fluorescent screen.

f) You are now able to obtain a sharply focused spot and to move the spot up and down and sideways by means of the X- and Y-SHIFT controls.

B2.3 How to obtain a horizontal trace

a) Turn the X-SHIFT control until the spot is at the left-hand edge of the screen. Now turn the control so that the spot moves at constant velocity across the screen. When the spot reaches the right-hand edge of the screen, make it 'fly back' to the starting position as quickly as possible. Do this several times — left to right at constant velocity, then right to left as quickly as possible. You are making the spot trace out a horizontal line across the screen.

b) `You can do the same thing with the Y-SHIFT control to trace out a line in the vertical direction. By manipulating both controls together, the spot can be made to trace out any desired pattern.

c) Next switch the TIME/CM (or TIME-BASE) to ON, and set the control to a slow speed, say about 100 ms. You will find that the internal time-base circuitry is doing what you yourself were doing when you rotated the X-SHIFT control. The spot will be tracing out a horizontal line, moving from left to right at constant velocity and flying back from right to left extremely rapidly

d) The speed at which the spot moves from left to right is controlled by the TIME/CM switch. See what happens with the switch at different settings. Find out the effect of rotating the VARIABLE or FINE time-base control. Also, try the effect of a control marked VELOCITY, if one is fitted.

e) When you have obtained a horizontal trace, see how it can be moved up and down and sideways by means of the Y- and X-SHIFTS, and see how it can be stretched or compressed by means of the control marked X-GAIN.

B2.4 How to measure a voltage

a) Set the AC/DC switch to DC. Connect a 9 V battery to the INPUT terminals, as indicated in fig. B2.2. Notice the effect on a spot or line trace: the trace moves either up or down, depending upon the battery polarity at the INPUT terminal. By using batteries of different e.m.f.'s, you will find that the movement of the spot or line is proportional to the e.m.f. of the battery.

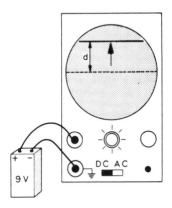

Fig. B2.2 Using an oscilloscope to measure d.c. voltage.

b) Try out the effects of switching to different VOLT/CM settings and rotating the FINE GAIN control, if one is fitted.

c) Since the up or down motion of the trace is proportional to the applied voltage, the oscilloscope can be used as a voltmeter. Furthermore, an oscilloscope acts as a very good voltmeter, because it has a very high resistance – see Section G for the importance of this.

d) In order to use the instrument as a voltmeter, it must be calibrated. This can be done by applying known voltages to the INPUT terminals and observing the movements of the trace. When this is done you should not alter the settings of controls such as INPUT SENSITIVITY, FINE GAIN, etc. You will probably find settings on these knobs marked CAL or VOLTS, etc. When the knobs are in these positions, the VOLTS/CM switch settings should give the voltage calibration directly.

e) Some instruments have a calibrated Y-SHIFT control. If your 'scope has one of these, the applied voltage will cause the trace to move up or down. You then rotate the Y-SHIFT control knob to return the trace to its initial position, and read off the corresponding voltage from the calibration on the Y-SHIFT scale.

B2.5 How to obtain a sine wave

a) Switch the AC/DC switch to AC. Obtain a spot on the screen, and hold a
    finger against the input terminal as shown in fig. B2.3. You should observe a
    vertical trace, the length of which can be varied by means of the VOLTS/CM
    switch settings. This trace is caused by your body acting as an aerial to the
    electromagnetic waves emitted by the power wiring in the room. The waves
    have a frequency of 50 Hz. They induce a voltage at this frequency into your
    body, and you are coupling a fraction of this voltage into the oscilloscope by
    means of your finger.

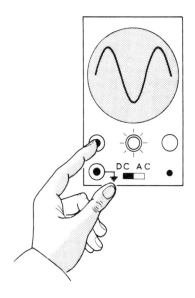

Fig. B2:3 Injecting a sine wave.

b) You can now switch the time-base to ON. This will give you a horizontal
    trace on which your finger is superimposing a vertical or Y deflection of the
    beam. The combined effect is a sine-wave trace on the screen. If the internal
    trigger circuits are operating correctly, this should be steady when the
    TRIGGER switch is set to INTERNAL or AUTO. A VELOCITY, FINE
    FREQUENCY, or SYNC control will help stabilise the trace, if one of these
    is fitted. A more reliable method of injecting a 50 Hz signal at the input ter-
    minals is by means of a low-voltage a.c. supply.

c) Some CRO's have a terminal marked SWEEP OUTPUT, TIME-BASE, or with
    a zig-zag line; the instrument shown in fig. B2.1 has this facility. The time-
    base is brought out to this terminal. If such a terminal is fitted to your

oscilloscope, connect it to the INPUT terminal as shown in fig. B2.4. The shape or 'waveform' of the time-base voltage will appear on the screen. The 'flyback' or vertical part of the trace may be so rapid that it is invisible.

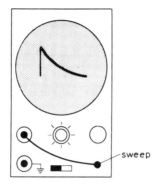

Fig. B2.4 How to show a saw-tooth waveform.

B2.6 How to measure time

a) Connect the output from a low-voltage a.c. source to the input of your oscilloscope. You may use an audio-frequency signal generator – see Section B3. Obtain a stable trace of a sine wave.

b) Adjust the VOLTS/CM control to obtain a suitable amplitude, and adjust the X-GAIN and X-SHIFT controls so that two consecutive peaks on the trace are separated by 5 cm – see fig. B2.5. Now the frequency of the applied voltage is 50 Hz. This means that there are 50 complete periods of change every second; thus one complete period lasts 1/50 second. Also, we can see that, since one complete period occupies 5 cm of the screen, the sideways velocity of the spot is 5 cm in (1/50) second or 250 cm/s. Alternatively, the TIME/CM is (1/250) s/cm.

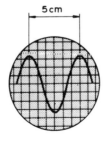

Fig. B2.5 Using a 50 Hz signal to calibrate an oscilloscope for time measurement.

c) We can now use the oscilloscope to measure time, for the continual sideways excursions of the electron beam are like the ticks of a clock.

d) The time calibration of an oscilloscope depends upon the setting of the TIME-BASE control, a FINE time-base control, if fitted, and the setting of the X-GAIN control. You will probably find that the TIME-BASE control is calibrated in 'times per cm'; if so, you will need to know how to set the FINE and X-GAIN controls before you can rely on the calibration. The correct settings can usually be found from the labelling of the control scales.

B2.7 Experiments with the CRO

Experiment 1 Connect an audio-frequency generator (described in Section B3) to the oscilloscope input, and obtain a stable trace at a frequency of about 10 kHz. Set the controls to the 'calibration' position, and find the time taken for one complete cycle of the waveform on the screen. Check the frequency indication on the oscillator dial with that derived from the oscilloscope trace.

If the time-base is uncalibrated, set the oscillator frequency at 1 kHz and obtain a stable trace with one complete cycle occupying 4 cm of the screen. Now increase the oscillator frequency until a stable trace is obtained with twice as many cycles as before. One complete cycle will now take up 2 cm on the screen, so the frequency will be twice as great as before, that is, 2 kHz. Check that the oscillator dial setting is 2 kHz. Do the same to obtain stable traces at 3 kHz, 4 kHz, etc., and check each oscillator dial setting. In this way, you are calibrating the oscillator dial against its 1 kHz setting.

Experiment 2 Assemble the *relaxation-oscillator* circuit shown in fig. B2.6 on an S-DeC, and connect its output to the oscilloscope. (The operation of this circuit

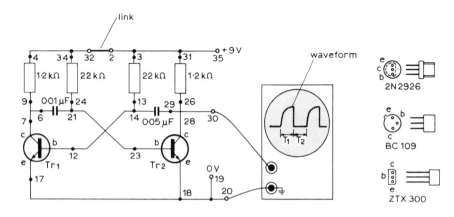

Fig. B2.6 Relaxation oscillator circuit and base views of some suitable transistors (c = collector, b = base, e = emitter).

is described in Section J.) Suitable transistors are shown for this circuit. You will notice that the circuit produces an approximately square waveform when the output is taken from the points shown. Measure the times T_1 and T_2 using the calibrated oscilloscope time-base.

Experiment 3 Switch off the internal time-base and obtain a sharply focused spot on the screen. Then connect the output from a low-voltage a.c. supply to both the X- and Y-input terminals. The input to the X-amplifier will pull the beam to and fro in the horizontal direction, while the input to the Y-amplifier will pull the beam to and fro in the vertical direction. The result of these two motions will be a straight line inclined to the horizontal. The inclination of the line will depend upon the relative sensitivities of the X- and Y-amplifiers.

You may find that instead of a straight-line trace, you get an ellipse or oval trace. This is often found in all but the highest-quality instruments and is caused by circuit imperfections in the amplifiers which apply the two signals to the CRO deflector plates slightly out of step with each other.

Connect the a.c. supply to the X-input and an audio-oscillator output to the Y-input, as shown in fig. B2.7. If one of the oscillator terminals is earthed, make sure that it is connected to an earthed terminal on the oscilloscope. Tune the oscillator to 50 Hz, 100 Hz, 150 Hz, 200 Hz, etc., and observe the traces.

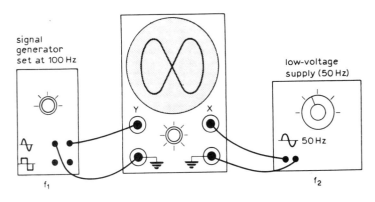

Fig. B2.7 How to show Lissajous figures.

The traces you are finding are called '*Lissajous figures*'. How could you use them to calibrate an oscillator frequency dial in terms of the frequency applied to the Y-input? It will help you to know that, when the frequency f_1 is twice that of f_2, the trace is like that in fig. B2.7 — a figure of eight on its side. Note that there are two loops touching the top of the screen and one at the side, and this is the ratio of f_1 to f_2, that is 2 to 1. How many loops are there touching the top of the screen when $f_1 = 150$ Hz?

B2.8 Special facilities on oscilloscopes

Some CRO's have two electron beams and are therefore called *'double-beam'* *oscilloscopes*. Both beams are operated by the same time-base circuitry, so that their horizontal motions are identical, but the FOCUS and BRIGHTNESS controls are sometimes separate. There is always a separate Y-amplifier input for each beam, so that two signals can be observed and measured simultaneously on the screen.

Care is needed when using double-beam CRO's, because of the fact that one of each pair of input terminals is usually earthed or connected internally to the metal case of the instrument. This results in each pair of inputs having a common terminal. If *coaxial* input sockets are provided — see Section B3.4 — the outer sheath of the socket is the common terminal.

B3 THE SIGNAL GENERATOR

B3.1 General description of signal generators

These are instruments which provide a continuously varying voltage across a pair of output terminals. The voltage usually varies *sinusoidally*, but it is sometimes possible to switch the output on some signal generators to produce a *square-wave* output.

The calibrations on the dial of a typical signal generator or oscillator producing waves in the *audio-frequency* (a.f.) range are shown in fig. B3.1. The audio-frequency range is the range over which the ear can detect sound waves, that is, from about 30 Hz to about 20 kHz. Generators which produce signals having frequencies in the range of thousands to millions of hertz are called 'r.f.' *(radio-frequency)* generators, since radio apparatus is sensitive to *electro-magnetic waves* with these orders of frequency. Generators of signals in the frequency range of tens of millions of hertz are called 'v.h.f.' *(very-high-frequency)* generators. Generators of waves in the range of hundreds of millions of hertz are called 'u.h.f.' *(ultra-high-frequency)* generators.

Fig. B3.1 The appearance of an audio-frequency signal generator. *(Courtesy Eagle International)*

Remember:

One thousand hertz = 1 kilohertz = 1 kHz = 10^3 Hz.

One million hertz = 1 megahertz = 1 MHz = 10^6 Hz.

One thousand million hertz = 1 gigahertz = 1 GHz = 10^9 Hz.

B3.2 Using an audio-frequency signal generator

The controls usually consist of the following (see fig. B3.1).

a) A switch to enable you to choose a particular frequency range.

b) A knob to 'tune' the instrument to the desired frequency — the large dial in fig. B3.1.

c) An output-voltage control, or 'volume control'. The mains on–off switch might be connected to this control just as on a radio or TV set. Sometimes more than one 'volume' control is fitted, in order to make possible 'coarse' and 'fine' control of the output-voltage amplitude. One of these controls might be called an ATTENUATOR and be calibrated in dB (decibels), which is a unit for comparing the ratio of two quantities. When the attenuator control is set to zero, the output voltage is at a maximum. The voltage is reduced as more and more attenuation is switched in.

d) Output terminals, one of which may be at earth voltage. The terminals may be simple screw types or coaxial-cable sockets — see Section B3.4. Remember that the outer lead on a coaxial cable is always earthed.

You may find a *resistance* (or to be technically correct, an *impedance*) expressed in 'ohms' marked on the front panel near the output terminals. This is the output resistance (or impedance) of the instrument. Output impedance is the a.c. analogy of the internal resistance of a d.c. battery or power supply. A generator will provide maximum power output when connected to a circuit or *load* equal to its output impedance — see experiment 2 in Section B3.3.

You may find several pairs of output terminals corresponding to different output resistances, e.g. 60 Ω or 600 Ω. Alternatively, there may be only one pair of terminals and a switch to enable you to choose one of several output impedances.

e) A separate EARTH terminal marked E, or ⏚, /⟋⟋⟋/ etc. may be provided, especially if the instrument does not have a coaxial-cable output socket.

B3.3 Experiments with an a.f. signal generator

Experiment 1 Connect the output from an a.f. generator to an oscilloscope, and observe the effects of changing the output-voltage amplitude and the frequency. Note that, if one of the output terminals is earthed, it must be connected to the earthed terminal on the oscilloscope.

Experiment 2 Connect a loudspeaker to the output terminals of the generator. If possible, try and choose a speaker whose resistance (impedance) is equal to the output resistance (impedance) of the generator. For example, choose a 75 ohm speaker for a 60 ohm generator, or a 4 ohm speaker for a 5 ohm generator. If the speaker resistance is much lower than the output resistance of the generator, it might help to connect a step-down transformer − see Section E − between the generator and the speaker. If you have a number of spare transformers, you might find a suitable one by trial and error. By using a transformer in this way, you are 'matching' the impedance of the generator to that of the speaker. The arrangement is shown in fig. B3.2, and in this case the transformer is acting as a *matching transformer.*

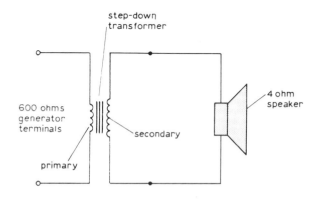

Fig. B3.2 Using a speaker-matching transformer.

B3.4   Coaxial-cable connectors

'Coax' is a special type of twin-lead cable. As shown in fig. B3.3, it consists of a central core lead which is completely surrounded by a sheath of woven copper

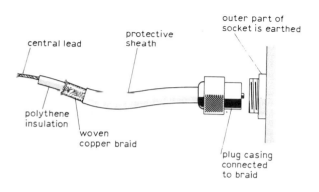

Fig. B3.3 How a coaxial-cable connection is made.

braid. The twin leads are insulated from one another by polythene, and the whole is surrounded by a protective plastics sheath.

Coax cables are usually connected together by means of coaxial plugs and sockets in such a way that the woven copper braid is earthed. This electrical connection to earth keeps the voltage of the braid at a constant (earth) voltage. Since the copper braid is earthed, it screens the central lead from stray electromagnetic fields which might induce unwanted voltages in it. This is known as 'pick-up'. A coaxial cable is used to reduce pick-up between the aerial and a TV set.

If the instrument you are using does not have a coaxial plug fitted to it, then crocodile clips may be used to make the connections to the coax, as shown in fig. B3.4.

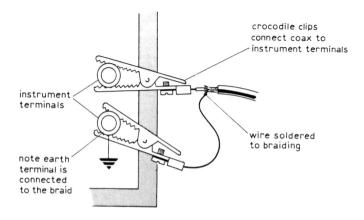

Fig. B3.4 How crocodile clips are used to connect a 'coax' to an instrument.

B4 THE MULTIMETER

B4.1 General description

This instrument is a 'must' for the electronics amateur and specialist alike. It combines in one case the basic instruments for the measurement of *voltage, current,* and *resistance.* The simple theory of the design of *voltmeters, ammeters,* and *ohmeters* is described in Section G, together with an idea for the design of a multimeter. For the present, a general description of the appearance of multimeters is given.

B4.2 The Avometer

One of the most popular types of good-quality multimeter is the *Avometer,* or simply AVO, named after the initial letters of amps, volts, and ohms. The basis of this instrument is a sensitive and robust meter; in fact, the meter is generally a *microammeter,* meaning that it responds to currents as small as a few millionths of an ampere (μA). Series and shunt resistances to the meter movement can be switched in so that the instrument acts as a multi-range ammeter and voltmeter. In order that a.c. quantities can be measured as well as d.c. quantities, *rectifier diodes* are included in the internal circuits – see Section G. The meter also contains a replaceable battery or batteries to enable resistance to be measured.

There are several models of the Avometer available. One type is shown in fig. B4.1 and has two main switches. On one switch you will notice DC RANGE marked. If this switch is set to the DC position, the other switch can be used to select one of a number of d.c. voltage and current ranges. On the other switch you will see AC RANGE marked. If this switch is set to the AC position, the other switch can be used to select one of a number of a.c. voltage and current ranges. In addition, one switch may be set to RESISTANCE and the other used to choose one of a number of resistance ranges. When used to measure ohms, the meter must be adjusted to give full-scale deflection (f.s.d.) with the meter terminals short-circuited. Small variable resistances mounted behind the front panel and connected to small control knobs enable this zero-adjustement to be made. You will notice that the resistance scales start with zero on the right-hand side of the scale, unlike the scales for current and voltage. The reason for this is explained in Section G.

B4.3 Reading the scale of a multimeter

It is easy to interpret the scale readings on a multimeter. For example, suppose that the instrument is switched to the 100 V d.c. f.s.d. (full-scale deflection) range and that the needle moves to 6.5 on a scale calibrated 10 V f.s.d. Since the

Fig. B4.1 Avometer Model 8. *(Courtesy Avometer Ltd)*

10 V f.s.d. is to be interpreted as 100 V f.s.d., the indicated 6.5 V must actually mean that a voltage of 65 V is being measured.

Most of the scale factors involve 'tens', that is, 0.1, 10, 100, etc. However, 'threes' are sometimes used. For instance, suppose the meter indicates a current of 2.5 on a current range which has an f.s.d of 3 when the meter is switched to the 0.3 mA range; in this case, the reading corresponds to a current of 0.25 mA or 250 μA.

B4.4   The cut-out on a multimeter

Good-quality multimeters have built into them a means of protecting the sensitive meter movement. On some Avometers this is a *cut-out* consisting of an electromagnetic switch which operates when too much current flows through the movement. If you see the cut-out operate, disconnect the meter, replace the cut-out button by depressing it, and take a new reading with the instrument switched to a much higher range. The cut-out acts only as a first line of defence against misuse; it will be too slow to protect the instrument against serious overload.

Remember:

When using a multimeter to measure an unknown current or voltage, always switch to the highest possible range at first. If you have chosen a range which is too high, you can then switch down to a lower one which is more suitable for the current or voltage which is being measured.

B4.5 Two types of multimeter

Fig. B4.2 shows a popular type of multimeter. It is 'pocket-size' and most probably the type you will be using in this course. These meters generally incorporate what is known as 'overload protection', usually consisting of protective diodes across the coil of the meter.

Fig. B4.2 A portable multimeter suitable for work in electronics. *(Courtesy Eagle International)*

A type of multimeter which is becoming more common in the laboratory and workshop, and which you may have the opportunity of using, is shown in fig. B4.3. It is known as a *digital multimeter*, since the readings do not appear on a meter scale but appear as numbers (digits) in gas-filled *numicator tubes* or, more recently, on *solid-state light arrays*. Digital instruments are much quicker to use, except that the position of the decimal point must be worked out for some instruments.

1 What is the quantity and what is the value being measured by the digital multimeter in fig. B4.3?

Fig. B4.3 Digital Avometer. *(Courtesy Avometer Ltd)*

Most electronic voltmeters are multimeters too, since they can be used over a number of different ranges. They are sometimes used for a.c. or d.c. voltage measurement only, although some instruments enable either quantity to be measured. The same instrument may also have the facility for measuring resistance.

A d.c. multimeter sometimes has a switch to enable you to alter the polarity of the terminals. for example, if a meter is switched to DC+ and a 0–10 V d.c. range, the needle on the meter will move backwards if you connect a 6 V battery to the terminals the wrong way. Instead of disconnecting the battery and reversing the connections, all you need to do is to switch the meter to DC−. You should not use the reverse switch deliberately, since the needle may suffer damage if it strikes the stop. However, if you were unsure of the polarity of the connections from your 6 V battery, then the best procedure would be to switch the voltmeter to either DC+ or DC− on the highest voltage range, say 500 V f.s.d. Then, if your guess at the polarity was incorrect, the needle would not have much travel to carry out in the reverse direction, so it would not come to any harm.

If the meter measures a.c. voltage, then the calibrations will usually be the r.m.s. values of the voltage. If a peak voltage is being measured, then it will definitely say so on the dial.

B4.6   Electronic voltmeters

The most serious limiting factor in the use of a moving-coil multimeter for the measurement of voltage is the rather low resistance the meter presents to the circuit across which it is measuring the voltage. Ideally, voltmeters should have an infinitely high resistance so that they do not draw any current from the circuit to which they are connected. (This problem is discussed more fully in Section G.) A meter which has a resistance of 10000 ohms cannot give an accurate figure of the voltage across a resistance of this order of magnitude, since the meter seriously *shunts* the resistance. An important measure of the *loading* effect of a voltmeter on a circuit is the *ohms-per-volt* (o.p.v.) rating of the meter. The higher the ohms-per-volt rating, the better the meter for measuring voltage. A poor multimeter may have an o.p.v. rating of as low as 4000 when switched to *volts*, whereas an electronic multimeter is likely to have an o.p.v. rating of one million ohms (1 megohm).

Originally, voltmeters with a high resistance were called *'valve' voltmeters*, since valves were, and still are in some cases, used in the internal circuitry. Nowadays, *field-effect transistors* and *integrated-circuits* are used.